LET'S SING TOGETHER

102 Most Popular Children's Songs

Volume I

Kidfest
INTERNATIONAL

Producer: Avshalom Rubin
Illustrator: Irina Karkabi
Re-writter of Lyrics & Musical Arranger: A. Avi-Eyal
Editor: Ralph Stein
Art Director: Arieh Bodian
Musical Director: Roni Weiss
Recording Producer: Zvika Kagan
Book Designer: Yossi Silber
Graphics: Sigal Singer

ISBN 965-312-003-4

Produced by I.C.F. Inc. P.O.Box 1528 Radio City Station N.Y.C., N.Y. 10101
Kidfest International is a registered trade mark of
International Children's Festival Inc.
Cat. No. B-43501

Contents

SKIP TO M' LOO

Loo, loo, skip to m' loo,
Loo, loo, skip to m' loo,
Loo, loo, skip to m' loo,
Skip to m' loo, my darling.

Lost my partner, what'll I do?
Lost my partner, what'll I do?
Lost my partner, what'll I do?
Skip to m' loo, my darling.

I'll get another one prettier than you,
I'll get another one prettier than you,
I'll get another one prettier than you,
Skip to m' loo, my darling.

Lost my partner, what'll I do?
Lost my partner, what'll I do?
Lost my partner, what'll I do?
Skip to m' loo, my darling.

Loo, loo, skip to m' loo,
Loo, loo, skip to m' loo,
Loo, loo, skip to m' loo,
Skip to m' loo, my darling.

7

OLD MACDONALD HAD A FARM

Old MacDonald had a farm,
Ee-igh, ee-igh, oh!
And on this farm he had some chicks,
Ee-igh, ee-igh, oh!
With a chick, chick here,
And a chick, chick there,
Here a chick, there a chick,
Everywhere a chick, chick.
Old MacDonald had a farm,
Ee-igh, ee-igh, oh!

Old MacDonald had a farm,
Ee-igh, ee-igh, oh!
And on this farm he had some ducks,
Ee-igh, ee-igh, oh!

With a quack, quack here,
And a quack, quack there;
Here a quack, there a quack,
Everywhere a quack, quack,
Chick, chick here,
Chick, chick there,
Here a chick, there a chick,
Everywhere a chick, chick.
Old MacDonald had a farm,
Ee-igh, ee-igh, oh!

Old MacDonald had a farm,
Ee-igh, ee-igh, oh!
And on this farm he had some turkeys,
Ee-igh, ee-igh, oh!
With a gobble, gobble here,
And a gobble, gobble there;
Here a gobble, there a gobble,
Everywhere a gobble, gobble,

Quack, quack here,
Quack, quack there;
Here a quack, there a quack,
Everywhere a quack, quack,
Chick, chick here,
Chick, chick there,
Here a chick, there a chick,
Everywhere a chick, chick.
Old MacDonald had a farm,
Ee-igh, ee-igh, oh!

Old MacDonald had a farm,
Ee-igh, ee-igh, oh!
And on this farm he had some pigs,
Ee-igh, ee-igh, oh!
With an oink, oink here,
And an oink, oink there,
Here an oink, there an oink,
Everywhere an oink, oink,
Gobble, gobble here, etc.

Old MacDonald had a farm,
Ee-igh, ee-igh, oh!
And on this farm he had some cows,
Ee-igh, ee-igh, oh!
With a moo, moo here,
And a moo, moo there, etc.

9

HUMPTY DUMPTY

Humpty Dumpty sat on a wall,
Humpty Dumpty had a great fall;
All the King's horses and all the King's men
Couldn't put Humpty Dumpty together again.

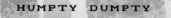

HUMPTY DUMPTY

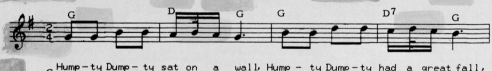

Hump—ty Dump—ty sat on a wall, Hump—ty Dump—ty had a great fall,

All the King's horses and all the King's men Couldn't put Hump—ty Dump—ty to

—geth—er a—gain.

HOT CROSS BUNS!

Hot cross buns!
Hot cross buns!
One a penny, two a penny,
Hot cross buns!
If you have no daughters,
If you have no daughters,
If you have no daughters,
Then give them to your sons;
But if you have none of these little elves,
Then you must eat them all yourselves.

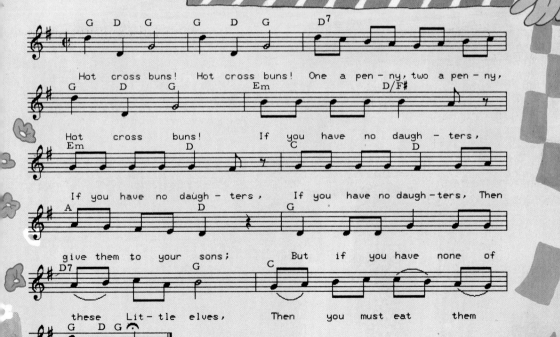

HARK, HARK, THE DOGS DO BARK

Hark, hark, the dogs do bark,
The beggars are coming to town,
Some in rags and some in bags,
And some in velvet gowns.

Hark, Hark, the dogs do bark, The beg-gars are com-ing to town, Some in rags and some in bags, And some in vel-vet gowns.

I HAD A LITTLE NUT-TREE

I had a little nut-tree, and nothing would it bear
But a silver nutmeg and a golden pear;
The King of Spain's daughter came to visit me,
And all for the sake of my little nut-tree.

I had a lit-tle nut-tree, and noth-ing would it bear
but a sil-ver nut-meg and a gold-en pear; The
King of Spain's daugh-ter came to vis-it me, And
all for the sake of my lit-tle nut-tree.

I LOVE LITTLE PUSSY

I love little pussy
Her coat is so warm
And if I don't hurt her,
She'll do me no harm.
She'll sit by the fire
And I'll give her some food
And pussy will love me
Because I am good.

love lit-tle pus-sy Her coat is so warm And

if I don't hurt her, she'll do me no harm. She'll sit by the fire And I'll

give her some food And pus-sy will love me Be-cause I am good.

14

JACK AND JILL

Jack and Jill went up the hill
To fetch a pail of water.
Jack fell down, and broke his crown,
And Jill came tumbling after.

Up Jack got, and home did trot,
As fast as he could caper.
Went to bed, to fix his head,
With vinegar and brown paper.

Jill came in, and she did grin,
To see his paper plaster.
Mother vexed, did whip her next,
For causing Jack's disaster.

JACK BE NIMBLE

Jack be nimble,
Jack be quick,
Jack jump over the candle stick.

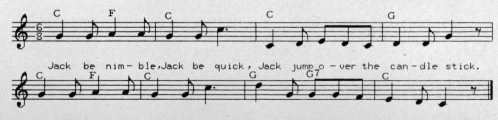

Jack be nim-ble, Jack be quick, Jack jump o-ver the can-dle stick.

Jack be nim-ble, Jack be quick, Jack jump o-ver the can-dle stick.

JACK SPRATT

Jack Spratt could eat no fat,
His wife could eat no lean;
And so between them both, you see,
They licked the platter clean.

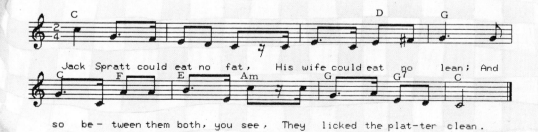

Jack Spratt could eat no fat, His wife could eat no lean; And so be-tween them both, you see, They licked the plat-ter clean.

KITTY ALONE

Saw a crow a-flying low,
Kitty alone, Kitty alone.
Saw a crow a-flying low,
Kitty alone a-lie.
Saw a crow a-flying low,
And a cat a-spying go,
Kitty alone a-lie,
Rukketa rye ree.

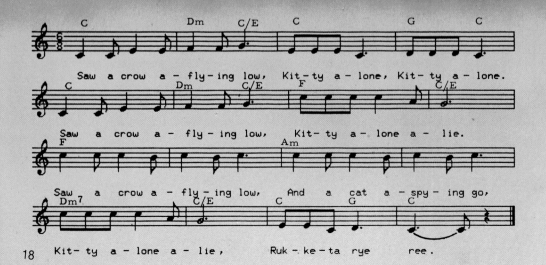

Saw a crow a — fly — ing low, Kit — ty a — lone, Kit — ty a — lone.

Saw a crow a — fly — ing low, Kit — ty a — lone a — lie.

Saw a crow a — fly — ing low, And a cat a — spy — ing go,

Kit — ty a — lone a — lie, Ruk — ke — ta rye ree.

THERE WAS A CROOKED MAN

There was a crooked man,
And he walked a crooked mile,
He found a crooked sixpence upon a crooked stile.
He bought a crooked cat,
Which caught a crooked mouse,
And they all lived together in a little crooked house.

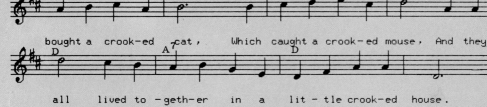

There was a crook-ed man, And he walked a crook-ed mile, He found a crook-ed six-pence u-pon a crook-ed stile. He bought a crook-ed cat, Which caught a crook-ed mouse, And they all lived to-geth-er in a lit-tle crook-ed house.

THERE WAS AN OLD WOMAN
WHO LIVED IN A SHOE

There was an old woman
Who lived in a shoe,
She had so many children
She didn't know what to do.
She gave them some broth without any bread,
Then she whipped them all soundly,
And sent them to bed.

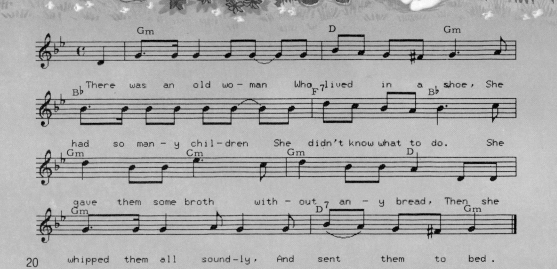

TOM, TOM, THE PIPER'S SON

Tom Tom, the piper's son,
Stole a pig and away he run!
The pig was eat,
And Tom was beat,
And Tom ran crying down the street.

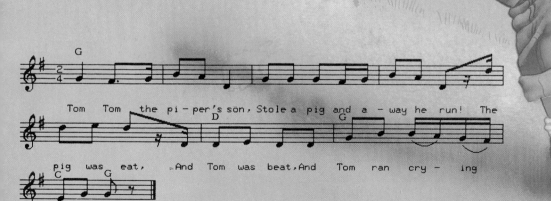

Tom Tom the pi-per's son, Stole a pig and a - way he run! The

pig was eat,   And Tom was beat, And Tom ran cry - ing

down the street.

ROW, ROW, ROW, YOUR BOAT

Row, row, row, your boat,
Gently down the stream,
Merrily, merrily, merrily, merrily,
Life is just a dream.

THERE WAS A LITTLE GIRL

There was a little girl
Who had a little curl
Right in the middle of her forehead,
And when she was good she was very, very good,
But when she was bad she was horrid!

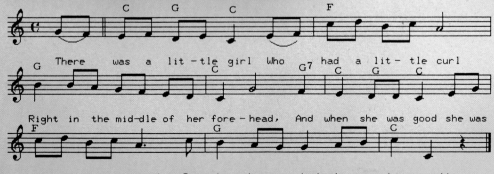

There was a lit-tle girl Who had a lit-tle curl
Right in the mid-dle of her fore-head, And when she was good she was
ver-y, ver-y good, But when she was bad she was hor-rid!

THREE LITTLE PIGGIES

There once was a sow who had three little piggies,
Three little piggies had she,
And the old sow always went, "oink, oink, oink,"
But the piggies went, "wee, wee, wee."

Now, one day one of these three little piggies
Said to his brothers, said he,
"Why don't we always go 'oink, oink, oink,'
It's so childish to go 'wee, wee, wee.'"

Now these three piggies grew skinny and sickly,
And skinny they well might be,
For they always tried to go "oink, oink, oink,"
When they should have gone, "wee, wee, wee."

And the three little piggies they upped and died,
A very sad sight to see.
So don't even try to go "oink, oink, oink,"
When you ought to go "wee, wee, wee."

THIS LITTLE PIG WENT TO MARKET

This little pig went to market,
This little pig stayed at home,
This little pig had roast beef,
This little pig had none,
And this little pig went wee, wee ... wee,
All the way home.

This lit-tle pig went to mar-ket, This lit-tle pig stayed at home, This lit-tle pig had roast beef, This lit-tle pig had none, And this lit-tle pig went wee, wee, wee, wee, wee, wee, All the way home.

THREE BLIND MICE

Three blind mice,
Three blind mice,
See how they run!
See how they run!
They all ran after the farmer's wife,
She cut off their tails with a carving knife;
Did you ever see such a sight in your life
As three blind mice?

THREE LITTLE KITTENS

Three little kittens
They lost their mittens,
And they began to cry,
Oh! mother dear,
We sadly fear,
Our mittens we have lost.
What! Lost your mittens?
You naughty kittens,
Then you shall have no pie.
Meeow, meeow, meeow, meeow,
Then you shall have no pie.

Three little kittens
They found their mittens,
And they began to cry,
Oh! mother dear,
See here, see here,
Our mittens we have found.
Put on your mittens,
You silly kittens,
And you shall have some pie.

Meeow, meeow, meeow, meeow,
And you shall have some pie.

SIMPLE SIMON

Simple Simon met a pieman,
Going to the fair;
Said Simple Simon to the pieman,
"Let me taste your ware."
Said the pieman to Simple Simon,
"Show me first your penny."
Said Simple Simon to the pieman,
"Indeed I have not any."

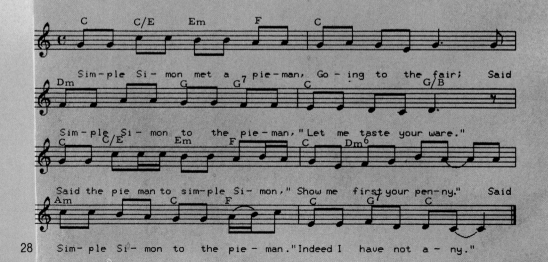

Sim-ple Si-mon met a pie-man, Go-ing to the fair; Said
Sim-ple Si-mon to the pie-man, "Let me taste your ware."
Said the pie man to sim-ple Si-mon," Show me first your pen-ny." Said
Sim-ple Si-mon to the pie-man."Indeed I have not a-ny."

TEN LITTLE INDIANS

One little, two little, three little Indians,
Four little, five little, six little Indians,
Seven little, eight little, nine little Indians,
Ten little Indian boys.

Ten little, nine little, eight little Indians,
Seven little, six little, five little Indians,
Four little, three little, two little Indians,
One little Indian boy.

One lit-tle, two lit-tle, three lit-tle In-dians,
Four lit-tle, five lit-tle, six lit-tle In-dians,
Sev-en lit-tle, eight lit-tle, nine lit-tle In-dians,
Ten lit-tle In-dian boys.

29

TO MARKET, TO MARKET

To market, to market, to buy a fat pig;
Home again, home again, jiggety jig;
To market, to market to buy a fat hog;
Home again, home again, jiggety jog.

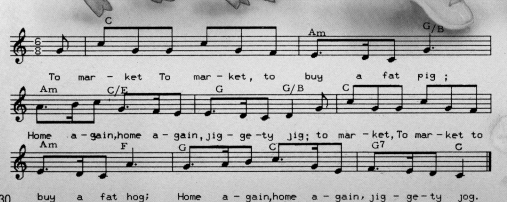

To mar-ket To mar-ket, to buy a fat pig;

Home a-gain, home a-gain, jig-ge-ty jig; to mar-ket, To mar-ket to

buy a fat hog; Home a-gain, home a-gain, jig-ge-ty jog.

WHAT ARE LITTLE BOYS MADE OF?

What are little boys made of ?
What are little boys made of ?
Frogs and snails and puppy-dogs' tails,
And that's what little boys are made of.

What are little girls made of ?
What are little girls made of ?
Sugar and spice and all that's nice,
And that's what little girls are made of.

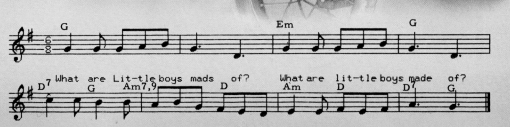

Frogs and snails and pup-py dogs' tails, And that's what lit-tle boys are made of.

WHERE DO ALL THE DAISIES GO?

Where do all the daisies go?
I know, I know;
Underneath the snow they creep,
And they hide their little feet,
That is where the daisies go,
Underneath the snow,
That is where the daisies go,
Underneath the snow.

Where do all the dai-sies go? I know, I know,
Un-der-neath the snow they creep, And they hide their lit-tle feet,
That is where the dai-sies go, Un-der-neath the snow,

That is where the dai-sies go, Un-der-neath the snow.

TWINKLE, TWINKLE, LITTLE STAR

Twinkle, twinkle little star,
How I wonder what you are,
Up above the world so high,
Like a diamond in the sky!
Twinkle, twinkle little star,
How I wonder what you are.

When the blazing sun has gone,
When he nothing shines upon,
Then you show your little light,
Twinkle, twinkle, all the night.
Twinkle, twinkle little star,
How I wonder what you are.

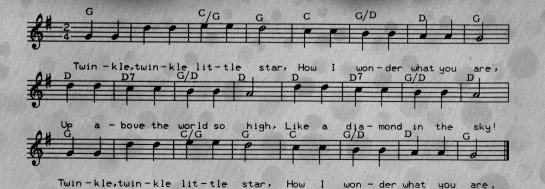

Twin-kle, twin-kle lit-tle star, How I won-der what you are,

Up a-bove the world so high, Like a dia-mond in the sky!

Twin-kle, twin-kle lit-tle star, How I won-der what you are.

A TISKET, A TASKET

A tisket, a tasket
A little yellow basket,
I wrote a letter to my love,
And on the way I dropped it,
I dropped it, I dropped it,
And on the way I dropped it.
A little boy (girl) picked it up
And put it in his (her) pocket.

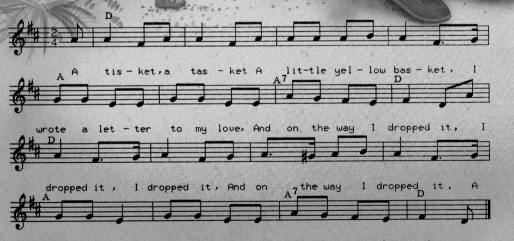

A tis-ket, a tas-ket A lit-tle yel-low bas-ket, I wrote a let-ter to my love, And on the way I dropped it, I dropped it, I dropped it, And on the way I dropped it. A lit-tle boy picked it up And put it in his pock-et.

YANKEE DOODLE

Oh Yankee Doodle came to town,
Upon a little pony!
He stuck a feather in his cap,
And called it macaroni!

Yankee Doodle Doodle Do
Yankee Doodle dandy;
All the lads and lassies are as
Sweet as sugar candy.

Father and I went down to camp
Along with Captain Goodwin
And there we saw the men and boys
As thick as hasty puddin'.

Yankee Doodle Doodle do
Yankee Doodle dandy
All the lads and lassies are as
Sweet as sugar candy.

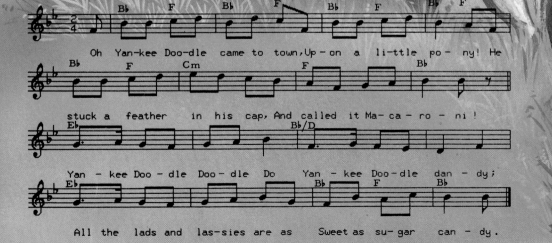

Oh Yan-kee Doo-dle came to town, Up-on a li-ttle po-ny! He
stuck a feather in his cap, And called it Ma-ca-ro-ni!
Yan-kee Doo-dle Doo-dle Do Yan-kee Doo-dle dan-dy;
All the lads and las-sies are as Sweet as su-gar can-dy.

ALL AROUND THE MULBERRY BUSH

Here we go round the mulberry bush,
The mulberry bush, the mulberry bush,
Here we go round the mulberry bush,
Early in the morning.

This is the way we wash our clothes,
We wash our clothes, we wash our clothes;
This is the way we wash our clothes,
Early Monday morning.

This is the way we iron our clothes,
We iron our clothes, we iron our clothes;
This is the way we iron our clothes,
Early Tuesday morning.

This is the way we scrub the floor,
We scrub the floor, we scrub the floor;
This is the way we scrub the floor,
Early Wednesday morning.

This is the way we mend our clothes,
We mend our clothes, we mend our clothes;
This is the way we mend our clothes,
Early Thursday morning.

This is the way we sweep the house,
We sweep the house, we sweep the house;

This is the way we sweep the house,
Early Friday morning.

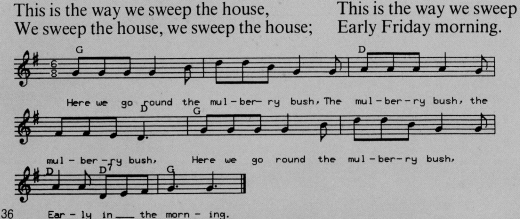

A-HUNTING WE WILL GO

Oh! A-hunting we will go,
Yes a-hunting we will go;
We'll catch a fox
And put him in a box
And then we'll let him go.

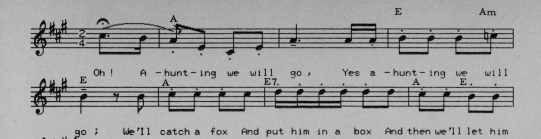

AS I WAS WALKING DOWN THE STREET

As I was walking down the street,
Down the street, down the street,
A pretty young girl I happened to meet
As I was walking down the street.

As I was walking down the street,
Down the street, down the street,
A nice young man I happened to meet
As I was walking down the street.

As I was walking down the street,
Down the street, down the street,
A big, black dog I happened to meet
As I was walking down the street.

As I was walking down the street,
Down the street, down the street,
A yellow cat I happened to meet
As I was walking down the street.

A, B, C

A, B, C, D, E, F, G,
H, I, J, K, L, M, N, O, P,
Q, R, S, and T, U, V,
W and X, Y, Z.
Happy, happy we shall be,
When we know our A, B, C.

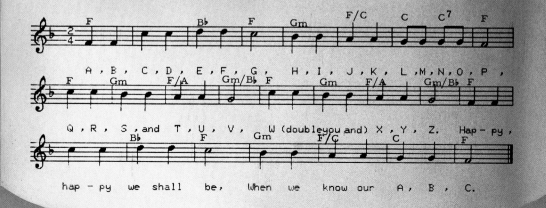

A, B, C, TUMBLE DOWN D

A, B, C,
Tumble down D,
The cat's in the closet and can't see me.

A, B, C,
Tumble down D,
The dog's in the dog-house and can't see me.

A, B, C,
Tumble down D,
The bird's in the birdnest and can't see me.

A, B, C,
Tumble down D,
The pig's in the pigstye and can't see me.

A, B, C,
Tumble down D,
The sheep's in the meadow and can't see me.

A, B, C,
Tumble down D,
The cow's in the cowshed and can't see me.

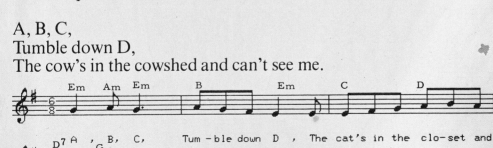

A, B, C, Tum—ble down D, The cat's in the clo—set and can't see me.

BAA! BAA! BLACK SHEEP

Baa! Baa! Black sheep
Have you any wool?
Yes, Sir,
Yes, Sir,
Three bags full.
One for the master and one for the dame,
One for the little boy who cries in the lane.
Baa Baa black sheep have you any wool?
Yes, Sir, Yes, Sir, Three bags full.

Baa! Baa! Black sheep Have you an-y wool? Yes, Sir, Yes, Sir,

Three bags full, One for the mas-ter and one for the dame,

One for the lit-tle boy who cries in the lane.

BOBBY SHAFTOE

Bobby Shaftoe went to sea,
Silver buckles on his knee;
He'll come back and marry me,
Pretty Bobby Shaftoe.

Bobby Shaftoe's fat and fair,
Combing down his yellow hair
He's my love for evermore,
Pretty Bobby Shaftoe.

Bob — by Shaf — toe went to sea, Sil — ver buck — les on his knee;
He'll come back and mar — ry me, Pret — ty Bob — by Shaf — toe.

BILLY BOY

Oh, where have you been, Billy Boy, Billy Boy,
Oh, where have you been, charming Billy?
I've been off to seek a wife,
She's the joy of my life,
She's a young thing and cannot leave her mother.

Did she ask you to come in, Billy Boy, Billy Boy?
Did she ask you to come in, charming Billy?
Yes, she asked me to come in.
There's a dimple on her chin,
She's a young thing and cannot leave her mother.

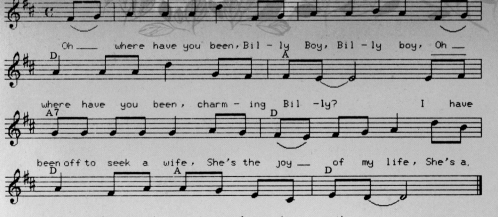

Oh __ where have you been, Bil-ly Boy, Bil-ly boy, Oh __
where have you been, charm-ing Bil-ly? I have
been off to seek a wife, She's the joy __ of my life, She's a,
young thing and can-not leave her moth-er .

THE CAT AND THE MOUSE

Pussy white so slyly comes
To catch the mousey grey,
But mousey hears her quietest tread
And quickly runs away;
Away! Away! Little mouse
Get out of sight and view
For pussy now is creeping up,
And she'll catch you.

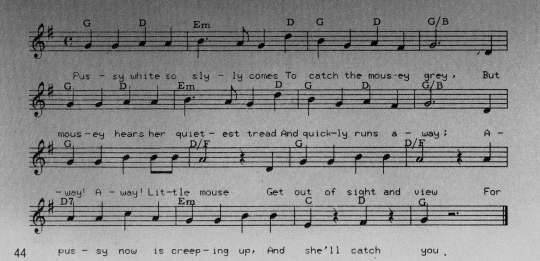

COCK-A-DOODLE-DOO

Cock-a-doodle-doo!
My lady's lost her shoe,
My master's lost his fiddling stick,
And doesn't know what to do.
Doesn't know what to do,
My master's lost his fiddling stick,
And doesn't know what to do.
Cock-a-doodle-doo!
What is my lady to do?
Till master finds his fiddling stick,
She'll dance without her shoe.
Dance without her shoe,
Till master finds his fiddling stick,
She'll dance without her shoe.

CURLY LOCKS

Curly Locks! Curly Locks! wilt thou be mine?
Ye shall not wash dishes and tend to the swine,
But sit on a cushion and sew a fine seam
And feast upon strawberries, sugar and cream.

Curl – y Locks! Cur – ly Locks! wilt thou be mine? Ye

shall not wash dish – es and tend to the swine, But

sit on a cush – ion and sew a fine seam And

feast up – on straw – ber – ries sug – ar and cream

DIDDLE, DIDDLE, DUMPLING

Diddle, diddle, dumpling, my son John,
Went to bed with his trousers on,
One shoe off and one shoe on,
Diddle, diddle, dumpling, my son John.

Did – dle, did – dle, dump – ling, my son John, Went to bed with his
trou – sers on, One shoe off and one shoe on,
Did – dle, did – dle, dump – ling, my son John.

DING, DONG, BELL

Ding, dong, bell,
Pussy's down the well;
Who put her in?
Little Johnny Green;
Who pulled her out?
Big John Stout.
What a naughty boy was that,
To drown poor little Pussy cat!
Who never did him any harm,
And killed the mice in his father's barn.

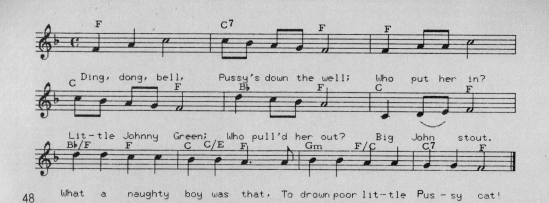

Ding, dong, bell, Pussy's down the well; Who put her in?
Lit-tle Johnny Green; Who pull'd her out? Big John stout.
What a naughty boy was that, To drown poor lit-tle Pus-sy cat!

EENSIE WEENSIE SPIDER

Eensie weensie spider
Went up the water spout,
Down came the rain and washed the spider out,
Up came the sun and dried up all the rain,
So the eensie weensie spider
Went up the spout again.

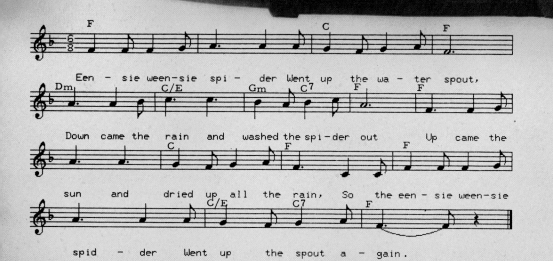

Een - sie ween-sie spi - der Went up the wa - ter spout,

Down came the rain and washed the spi-der out Up came the

sun and dried up all the rain, So the een - sie ween-sie

spid - der Went up the spout a - gain.

FIDDLE DEE DEE

Fiddle dee dee,
Fiddle dee dee,   × 2
The fly has married the bumblebee

Said the fly, said he,
"Will you marry me,
And live with me, sweet bumblebee?"

Fiddle dee dee,
Fiddle dee dee,
The fly has married the bumblebee,

Said the bee, said she,
"I'll live under your wing,
And you'll never know that I carry a sting."

So when the parson had joined the pair,
They both went out to take the air.

Fiddle dee dee,
Fiddle dee dee,
The fly has married the bumblebee.

And the flies did buzz, and the bells did ring,
Did ever you hear so merry a thing?

And then to think that of all the flies,
The bumblelee should marry the prize,

Fiddle dee dee,
Fiddle dee dee,   × 2
The fly has married the bumblebee.

50

Fid - dle -dee-dee, Fid - dle-dee-dee the fly has mar -ried the
bum - ble-bee Said the fly, said he, "Will you mar - ry me and
live with me, sweet bum - ble - bee?"

THE FARMER IN THE DELL

The farmer in the dell, the farmer in the dell,
High ho the derry oh, the farmer in the dell.

The farmer picks a wife, the farmer picks a wife,
High ho the derry oh, the farmer picks a wife.

The wife picks a child, the wife picks a child,
High ho the derry oh, the wife picks a child.

The child picks a nurse, the child picks a nurse,
High ho the derry oh, the child picks a nurse.

The nurse picks a dog, the nurse picks a dog,
High ho the derry oh, the nurse picks a dog.

The dog picks a cat, the dog picks a cat,
High ho the derry oh, the dog picks a cat.

The cat picks a rat, the cat picks a rat,
High ho the derry oh, the cat picks a rat.

The rat picks the cheese, the rat picks the cheese,
High ho the derry oh, the rat picks the cheese.

The cheese stands alone, the cheese stands alone,
High ho the derry oh, the cheese stands alone.

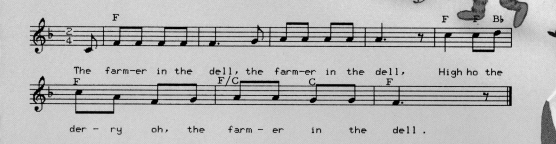

The farm-er in the dell, the farm-er in the dell, High ho the der-ry oh, the farm-er in the dell.

GOOSEY, GOOSEY, GANDER

Goosey, goosey, gander, whither do you wander?
Upstairs, downstairs and in the lady's chamber;
There I met an old man who wouldn't say his prayers,
I took him by the left leg and threw him down the stairs.

Goo - sey, goo - sey, gan - der, whit - her do you wan - der?

Up - stairs, down - stairs and in the lady's cham - ber

There I met an old man who woul - dn't say his prayers, I

took him by the left leg and threw him down the stairs.

GOOD MORNING TO YOU

Good morning to you,
Good morning to you,
We're all in our places
With sun-shining faces.
Is this not the way
To start a new day.

Let's start a new day.

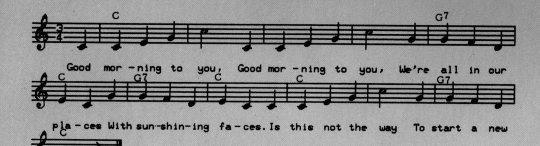

Good mor-ning to you, Good mor-ning to you, We're all in our

pla-ces With sun-shin-ing fa-ces. Is this not the way To start a new

day.

GEORGIE PORGIE

Georgie Porgie, pudding and pie,
Kissed the girls and made them all cry;
When the boys came out to play,
Georgie Porgie ran away.

GIRLS AND BOYS, COME OUT TO PLAY

Girls and boys, come out to play,
The moon is shining as bright as day.
Leave your supper and leave your sleep,
And join your friends in the street.

Come with a whoop, and come with a call,
Come with a good will or come not at all.
Up the ladder and down the wall,
A penny loaf will serve us all.
Girls and boys, come out to play
The moon is shining as bright as day

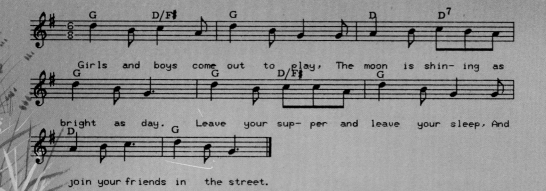

Girls and boys come out to play, The moon is shin- ing as
bright as day. Leave your sup- per and leave your sleep, And
join your friends in the street.

GOOD MORNING, MERRY SUNSHINE

Good morning, merry sunshine,
How did you wake so soon?
You've scared the little stars away,
And shined away the moon;
I saw you go to sleep last night,
Before I stopped my playing,
How did you get way over here,
And where have you been staying?

I never go to sleep, dear child,
I just go round to see
My little children of the east,
Who rise and watch for me;
I waken all the birds and bees
And flowers on the way,
And last of all the little child
Who stayed out late to play.

Good morn-ing, mer-ry sun-shine, How did you wake so soon? You've scared the lit-tle stars a-way, And shined a-way the moon; I saw you go to sleep last night, Be-fore I stopped my play-ing, How did you get way o-ver here, And where have you been stay-ing?

HEY, DIDDLE DIDDLE

Hey diddle diddle,
The cat and the fiddle,
The cow jumped over the moon;
The little dog laughed to see such fun,
And the dish ran away with the spoon.

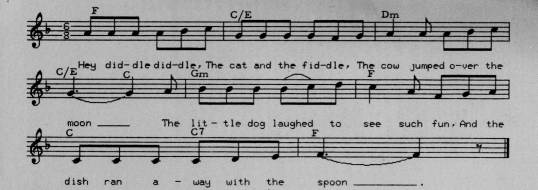

Hey did-dle did-dle, The cat and the fid-dle, The cow jumped o-ver the moon ___ The lit-tle dog laughed to see such fun, And the dish ran a-way with the spoon ___.

HICKORY, DICKORY, DOCK

Hickory, dickory, dock;
The mouse ran up the clock;
The clock struck "one",
The mouse ran down;
Hickory, dickory, dock.

Hick- o -ry, dick-o -ry, dock; The mouse ran up the

clock; The clock struck "one", The mouse ran down;

Hick - o - ry, dick- o - ry, dock.